Unjustified Joy

Leah Jeffery

Onwards and Upwards Publishers

3 Radfords Turf, Cranbrook, Exeter,
EX5 7DX, United Kingdom.
www.onwardsandupwards.org

First edition, published in the United Kingdom by Onwards and Upwards Publishers (2018).

ISBN: 978-1-78815-643-1
Typeface: Sabon LT
Graphic design: LM Graphic Design

Printed in the United Kingdom.

Endorsements

Leah Jeffery (now 32 years old) has written a short book detailing her own personal journey of faith and purpose through dealing with an unexpected chronic illness called Ankylosing Spondylitis. *Unjustified Joy* is honest, vulnerable and engaging. Her faith in Jesus through considerable trials at a young age encourages us all to be more purposeful, hopeful and joyful in the highs and lows of life.

Nicky Gumbel
Pioneer of the Alpha course
Vicar, Holy Trinity Brompton

Leah is always smiling. Her continuous radiant warmth conveys a picture that all is well – but in reality her story has significant complexity and pain. This story oozes with her smile while honestly telling the backstory. The bridge between the seeming disparity of these two dynamics is hope – hope that has been tested but found to be present. Her hope flows from the pages and inspires each of us that we can know its presence in our lives also.

Mark Pugh
Senior Pastor
Rediscover Church, Exeter

I couldn't stop reading when I first picked [this book] up. [It] took me on a journey with [Leah]. What a powerful account of trusting in God, waiting on Him, and resting in the hope He brings. I laughed and cried through [her] pain as [she] did, and rejoiced as [she] found joy when it felt lost.

Dr Ysanne Marville
Educational Psychologist

About the Author

Born in Cornwall and raised in West Sussex, the youngest of six children, Leah grew up in a Christian family who always found opportunity to connect with people from different cultures and backgrounds. This fuelled her desire to explore beyond her surroundings, and also to encourage unity in the church. Leah loved to paint and draw from a young age, so with a love of creative things, she later gained a university degree in Graphic Design, before taking the leap to move to Cairns in Queensland, Australia.

Australia brought a special sense of 'home' as she joined a church where family and unity were a main focus. Working in a sign and print company as a graphic designer eventually led to gaining Australian Citizenship.

After five years in Australia, some unexpected health issues led to Leah returning to the UK, where she now currently lives, in the county of Devon. Over those years, the difficult times were the moulding, shaping and testing of her faith.

To contact Leah, please write to:

Leah Jeffery
c/o Onwards and Upwards Publishers
3 Radfords Turf
Exeter
EX5 7DX

Or send an email to:

leahmaarit@hotmail.com

Contents

Unjustified Joy

Foreword by Pastor Helen Leafa

The book you hold in your hands is small but mighty, a lot like the author herself. As you read Leah's journey, her honesty and vulnerability will inspire you to trust in the authority of God's word and to receive His kindness and His goodness as refreshment and nourishment through even the most difficult places in your journey.

Before this book is finished, you will understand that Leah-Maarit Jeffery is one courageous Sheila – by the way, that's Aussie for 'chick'. Leah arrived in our country via an email sent to our church, all ready to bravely embark upon a new adventure. One of the first things I learnt about Leah was that she was a dreamer, with many a morning spent over a coffee and peanut butter toast, listening as she shared with us the wild and incredible dreams she'd had the night before. Needless to say, Leah fitted right in to our home, our hearts and the Rock Church, and we enjoyed some good, good times together over the years.

It was during this time with her Rock Church family that Leah first experienced the symptoms of AS.

We journeyed together during the 'pain in the neck times', the frustrating times of endless tests and unanswered questions, until it became obvious that she needed to return home to England to receive the treatment and care she needed. We were saddened to see Leah leave Australia, however I have learnt that destiny is often found in the relationships God brings into our lives to embrace in the season at hand, and the pleasures to enjoy in the fullness of that moment.

I was emotional reading Leah' story, as you can never truly understand what others go through unless you walk in their shoes. Reading this book helped me to walk in her shoes for a little while and from that gain greater empathy and understanding for those who experience chronic pain and illness.

I am so glad Leah has written the story of her health and shared with us her heart. You will get to know Leah a little more as you read her story. She is kind, she is brave, she is incredibly talented, she is funny, but most of all she is a faith-filled daughter of the most wonderful Papa God, whom she continues to cling to throughout life's journey. Our wonderful Papa has finished writing the story of Leah's life and her faith is not in vain. We are His word and our lives will not return to Him void, but will fulfil all He has written of us.

As an endorsement to this book and in expectation of what I believe our good Papa is going to do in and through Leah-Maarit Jeffery's life, I would like to share a prophetic dream/encounter I had regarding Leah earlier this year.

> *I saw you, Leah, stretched out across two seats of an aeroplane. There were two cabin lights shining on you, and you had a blanket covering you as you slept. I knew you had experienced pain in your neck and hip in the past so I knew that lying across the seats of an aeroplane would be difficult, yet there you were completely comfortable, completely rested and at peace. I asked the Holy Spirit what you were doing and immediately I knew you were flying somewhere on assignment. I was then led to pray specifically in relation to His call upon your life to the nations. Yes, you are called to the nations!*

> *Psalm 2:8 (TPT): "Ask me to give you the nations and I will do it, and they shall become 'your' legacy. Your domain will stretch to the ends of the earth."*

> *Leah, Holy Spirit said you are being raised up as you go. Healing is not your inheritance – your inheritance is the nations. In this vision I believe God was confirming His call upon your life. Regardless of what has tried to cripple you, the Father is working in you and as you remain in His peace He will take care of your physical body, as you go in Him – in rest.*

> *Amen – let it be according to your will and your word, Father.*

As you read this book, I pray you will be encouraged and inspired by Leah's story and by her faith. May it cause you to soar on eagle's wings as you see from a heavenly perspective all that our good Father is doing in your life and in the life of Leah.

Psalm 38.15
I Decree:
My hope is in You. Not just fingers crossed, hoping without cause to believe. No!
I watch. I linger. I wait.
Expecting. Believing. Knowing.
You hear me! Not just like a noise in the breeze, without attention. No!
You listen. You respond. You answer. Speaking. Singing. Blessing.

Elizabeth A. Nixon

Pastor Helen Leafa
Co-Senior Leader
Rock Church International

Unjustified Joy

1

A Real Pain in the Neck

I have finally decided that I should share the honest story of my health. I have moved around quite a lot, and my friends and family have been with me through different stages of the journey, but no one has seen me through it all. This book will be of interest to those who know me and wish to understand my condition better, but it will also be of help to anyone who is suffering with a chronic condition.

I have what's called *Ankylosing Spondylitis,* but from here on out, it shall be simply 'AS' (because kicking AS is what I do). You might already be asking, "Anky-what-now?" But I will start at the beginning...

2011. I honestly have no idea of the month or season. I was living in Cairns, Australia, aged twenty-five, and had been doing so for three years since leaving my home in England. Cairns really only has two seasons anyway: hot, or hotter and wet.

I had always been in very good health. In fact, I was that annoying person that verbally prided themselves on never getting sick every time the whole office went down with the flu. I worked in a quite compact office with three other graphic designers and it certainly wasn't difficult to catch something when it was going around. However, I just didn't get sick.

One morning I woke up for work like any other day. There was nothing special about that time or that day. However, as I got up, it became quickly evident that I couldn't move my neck more than thirty degrees without... *ou-ou-ouch!*

It was the worst feeling. It hadn't happened before, so I simply put it down to the fact that I would always sleep stomach down, with my neck cricked out to one side. I went to work as usual. Work was always fast-paced with regular customer interaction. Like anyone who has had a sore neck would know, it was frustrating. And not just frustrating for one day. It didn't go away. In fact, this bad neck hung around for three months before I gave up expecting it to fix itself.

So three months on, it was time to see a doctor. Australia's medical system is generally good. However, in my experience, when I wanted to see a doctor urgently and for free, after the usual couple of hours' wait in the queue I would often get the sense the doctor wanted me in and out as quickly as possible. I went to the 24-hour free doctor and explained my issue. He suggested a blood test, which seemed reasonable. I had no idea what he was testing for though. I complied and waited for the results over the next week. Then, when I returned, the tests had shown no result. So the doctor suggested a different blood test. Again, I complied and another week passed. I returned and still no result. A third blood test was taken, another week passed and yet another unhelpful result... At this point I was seeing a different doctor. She said that she wanted me to have a CAT scan, but that I was far too young because of the radiation effects, so I should just see the physiotherapist, with whom I would have five free sessions (covered by Medicare).

So the physiotherapy began. I quite enjoyed the feeling of being given this free care and felt really positive that it would help. I returned each week, a little sorer but felt sure it was because the physio was 'doing its thing'. The five weeks passed, and I began paying for my sessions. Absolutely no problem. Three months later, the physio said to me, "I'm sorry, but I think you are going to need something more than physiotherapy. Your neck just isn't moving. I recommend that you try the chiropractor."

On to the chiropractor. I actually loved going there. They only seemed to employ extremely friendly and extremely handsome chiropractors, which I'm quite sure was not coincidental. It didn't take long to feel that the whole staff knew who I was. My regular doctor was a friendly Canadian who seemed to enjoy trying out a new 'dad joke' on me every session. Before any treatment he took a few X-rays, which made me feel more confident about the situation. The experience was generally good, except for the 'cracking the neck' scenario. This involves the doctor holding the weight of your chin and the back of your head and giving your neck a quick unexpected twist. It was scary every time, and yes, it hurt, even though I was assured that it shouldn't cause any pain. Yet I would take a deep breath because I needed this neck fixed.

It didn't take long for the chiropractor to realise that I was going to be hard work, yet the team were convinced that if we just stuck at it two or three times a week, there was no reason that it shouldn't improve.

Leah-Maarit Jeffery

October 29, 2012 · Cairns, QLD, Australia · 👥 ▼

Feels like a mini explosion happens in my head every time I cough... Euurghh 😞

Time went on, and after about a year my leg started playing up a little. I really don't remember how this started at all. Perhaps it was just some small hip joint pains, which would have been barely noticeable in comparison with everything going on with my neck. But ever so gradually the hip got worse, and I developed a limp.

An excerpt from my diary on 17/03/13:

> *Feeling a bit better today. I woke up almost unable to move and my leg nearly gave way as I hobbled to the lounge. But once my muscles had got moving, I was OK by the time that I got to church. I was aware that I was able to move in the worship more freely than I have done this year so far. There's nothing more frustrating than struggling to worship because of pain, because that's the moment you want to give the pain to God. Asking Him to take it. You can tell yourself that you won't focus on your bad week or the way you feel emotionally because this is God's time. But you can't ignore pain. That is the moment that I realized that worship is not always changing how I feel. It is saying that despite how I feel, I know your great love for me surpasses my situation.*

> *Isaiah 40:30-31 says:*

> *"But those who hope in the Lord will renew their strength. They will soar on wings like eagles. They will run and not grow weary. They will walk and not be faint."*

> *I was led to this verse today as God gave me a clear picture in my mind. I questioned the fear I have of letting go for Him. Then I imagined an eagle. It was huge, and I was secure, riding on its back. The view was spectacular, of a sunset over the water and mountains. I was aware that this was not a perspective that I could possibly see with my feet on the ground. I just wanted to focus on the beautiful setting sun.*

13

> *Most importantly, it was not scary and it was not difficult. But it required a decision to not stay grounded.*

I wasn't exactly sure what that all meant at the time. But I felt reassured that all I needed to do was keep trusting and keep hoping, that God was not only with me in this but could give me a perspective and purpose greater than what I was seeing.

I was utterly determined to be patient. I took out healthcare insurance so that I could get a reduction on the cost. After a few months the doctor started giving me the odd free session. Perhaps he felt a little guilty that nothing was improving, I don't know. It wasn't just not improving; I realised it was getting worse. And the leg problem didn't make sense. They began working on my lower back also. The theory was that perhaps the neck problem was throwing my hip out, so if they sorted out the top, the rest would fall in line. I'm sure that's the very simplified version of what they had in mind, but it made sense at the time. The chiropractic 'neck crack' would on the odd occasion make me dizzy to the point of nearly passing out, but more often pushed me to tears. I don't think it was the pain in the moment as much as the frustration that I was holding myself together after the pain through a long day of work.

 Leah-Maarit Jeffery   •••
June 29, 2013 · Cairns, QLD, Australia · 🌐 ▾

Is it just coincidence that all 3 of the Chiropractors I've seen have been ridiculously good looking?

I think not.

Work was difficult on a daily basis – some days much worse than others, but I always seemed to get through the day. Sometimes it was tears in the bathroom, but more often it was tears on the drive home. It got to the point that the pain would make me cry, then sniffling tears would cause more pain, leading to more tears. A rotten cycle. Laughter was pain. *Every* movement was pain.

One thing that you learn when you have something you can't fix is that everyone around you is also struggling because they can't fix you. So that results in a whole lot of advice from people who are absolutely certain that "*this* is what will make you better". People are well-meaning, and I had to quickly learn to have grace for those people, but I also had to learn to say "no, thank you" without needing to explain my reasons for rejecting their advice. It turns out that a lot of people in Cairns are willing to try out what I would call 'mystic' healing methods, purely because someone has told them that it works. When you are desperate for relief, I can understand why someone would be willing to try anything. However, I said many no's to many suggestions and felt at peace to continue what I was doing patiently and, most importantly, to pray for answers and healing. I knew God was not freaking out, so I wasn't going to either.

Leah-Maarit Jeffery   ···

July 16, 2013 · Cairns, QLD, Australia · 🌏 ▾

When I'm told that getting very drunk will get my body moving again, I remember why I ignore all the many pieces of advice people give me.

One suggestion that seemed feasible was that I may have had a delayed reaction to the car and bike accidents that I had been through the year before (two separate accidents). It sounded possible but still didn't sit right with me. I had written my car off in a 180-degree spin off the main road. My car was wrecked but I was absolutely unscathed. I had been driving back from a church event, and after stepping out of the car in the ditch, I found myself laughing and thanking God that I was alive and not at all bothered about the car (until a week later, when I really mourned for my Mazda Mx6). I had not jolted my neck in the slightest. The second accident was coming off my moped after a hard brake at a roundabout in wet weather. I injured my leg on that one, but again, there was nothing that would have caused whiplash in my neck.

Still going to the chiropractor, the lovely Canadian took more X-rays. At this point I said, "Are you absolutely sure it couldn't be some kind of condition?" He replied, "Like what?" Of course, not having a clue, I just shrugged it off with, "I don't know…" He assured me that he didn't think it was any kind of condition. He showed me the X-ray of my neck and one bone was very thin. He told me that this was a congenital deformity that I had probably had my whole life and was now causing me issues. A regular X-ray wasn't going to cut it though.

He referred me to have an MRI scan. I booked this in and paid for it. I had never had one of these. I had only seen these machines on movie scenes in which cancer patients would go in, only to receive the bad news afterwards. The machine was a strange experience. Lying down and being put into the tunnel with a pair of headphones for music... Nice idea, but the machine noise was so loud. The music wasn't the greatest distraction anyway. Lying there for thirty minutes or so felt like an eternity.

 Leah-Maarit Jeffery   ...

July 22, 2013 · Cairns, QLD, Australia · 🌐 ▾

My pastor told me, "Do not look to the left or the right".
So I've been taking that seriously this year.

After all was over, days passed and the results came back. The report from the MRI doctor said that all was absolutely normal. *What? Normal?* No. Even my chiropractor was unhappy and challenged the report. The doctor admitted it could have been the position the scan was taken from. He rechecked the scans and made a different report, but only confirming what we already knew.

I had reached the point of being a self-confessed pill-popper; ibuprofen pills, that is. They were the closest thing to any kind of relief. The packet warned not to have any more than the recommended dose every three hours. My life became a repeated holding out for that three hours to pass so that I could have another dose. My head felt like a heavy aching weight unable to hold up for long. Someone likened the weight of a human head to that of a bowling ball, and from then it was all I could imagine; holding a bowling ball up with my neck every day. Thankfully, in Australia they sell ibuprofen in larger quantity value pots, so I wasn't killing my life savings in the process.

As the weeks continued on, the prayers became more fervent and I became more immobile. I have never been shown so much practical love as I was shown at this time. My boss felt that a better office chair could help, so he sent me to the shop with a decent budget to go and pick whichever one I liked. I picked the biggest and comfiest 'manager' chair, which made me feel a little guilty, having to fit it into our already packed office space. But it helped me so much to rest my neck back and just get through the day... One good friend surprised me one evening with bags of groceries just dropped at my door... Even jokes at my expense were exactly what I needed: friends doing impromptu robot dances or standing behind me saying, "Hey, Leah, look!" knowing full well I couldn't turn around and look. Yes, I needed these kinds of friends. I needed to laugh at my situation. I needed to tell customers at work that, "I fought with a kangaroo and the kangaroo won," because I had no better answer to give.

Leah-Maarit Jeffery
July 25, 2013 · Cairns, QLD, Australia · 🌐 ▾

Therefore we do not lose heart. Though outwardly we are wasting away, yet inwardly we are being renewed day by day. For our light and momentary troubles are achieving for us an eternal glory that far outweighs them all. So we fix our eyes not on what is seen, but on what is unseen, since what is seen is temporary, but what is unseen is eternal (2 Corinthians 4:16-18 NIV)

My chiropractor lost the battle. He finally decided, "I am going to write a letter to the GP. I'll mark it as urgent so that he reads it quickly. I want him to see you again."

So I went to the doctor. He did a few basic reflex and mobility tests. I explained my story so far, as I felt I had already done a thousand and one times to others. I don't remember what he said, but I do remember feeling he was about to turn me away without answers again.

Then he stopped and mumbled, "Can you just walk to that door and back?"

So I did.

He hadn't checked my walk until this point. His face changed and he continued, "I am going to get you to go to the Emergency department at the hospital. I will send them a fax now. Please go there in the next couple of hours."

2

Emergency

So that was it. I internally panicked. *Emergency?* It wasn't until later that I was told the only way to get hospital care immediately and for free is to go through Emergency, so it was a blessing in disguise. However, at this point, I was overwhelmed again. I drove back to work and explained that I had to go. Yes, I drove. Something I had become quite terrified of doing with a neck that wouldn't turn properly and excruciating pain at every roundabout and speed bump. I didn't feel that I had much choice at that point. I called a friend, and she offered to leave work and take me there. I went home, packed some clothes and went.

We waited the usual few hours to get seen. I thought I would maybe have some tests and then be back home that night. As we went through, they sat me on a bed and did the same standard reflex and mobility tests and asked all the usual generic questions I had been asked so many times. After some more waiting I was wheeled away on a hospital bed to get the CAT scan that I had been refused the year before. There I lay still while I had the scan. Then I continued to lie there waiting for what felt like forever. Finally, a group of doctors came in, didn't say a word, surrounded me and put me in a neck brace. "OK... this is exciting," I thought, having not been in any kind of hospital situation in my adult life. I was told I mustn't sit up. Then they took me back to the previous spot. Eventually nurses came to change my clothes, but realised my hoodie was not going to come off without me being allowed to move. Out came a large pair of scissors. *Oh no!* I was devastated! It was my favourite hoodie; I was more saddened than when my car had been written off.

Then it was off to the ward. I now realised I was staying the night. I didn't really have a clue what was happening and just went with the flow of it all. I shared a ward with perhaps five or so other men and women. I don't remember any of their faces though, as I had to lie flat. Staring at the ceiling was awfully boring and, dare I say, lonely. It was the weekend of the Cairns Show, in which a huge carnival of rides, events and fun comes to town. All the nurses were talking about it, which was a nice means of conversation but a stark reminder that I was not going to get to go this year.

I ended up in hospital for just three days. Three... very... long... days. It was quite the rollercoaster of experiences, and I was quite willing to just take what came with it. Again, bear in mind that this was the first hospital experience of my adult years. They did a few more X-rays and another MRI.

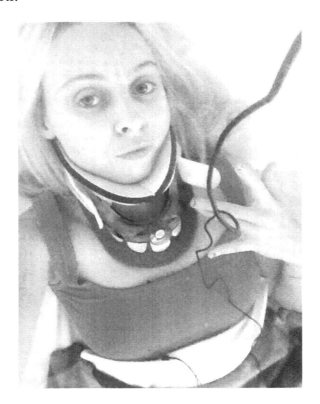

Every trip back to the ward was met with bed baths, roll over massages, catheters, pokes, prods, questions and a few events I just cannot bring myself to mention. A different set of nurses and doctors each day came to ask me the same questions.

One very abrupt Russian girl pulled my leg and asked, "Does this hurt?" *Yes, it blimmin' well does!* She was without a smile or change of tone in her voice as she talked to the other doctors and read my clipboard.

She then turned to ask me, "How long have you had rheumatoid arthritis?"

I was stunned at her question. I simply replied, "Um… I didn't know that I did."

She said nothing, put the clipboard back and walked off with her little team.

A few moments later I cried. *It must say that I have RA on my clipboard, and no one has told me yet. She must have let the cat out of the bag.* It made sense.

About thirty minutes later a nurse came in and told me that I didn't have RA and apologised on the other girl's behalf, insisting she wasn't a friendly doctor. *I'll say!*

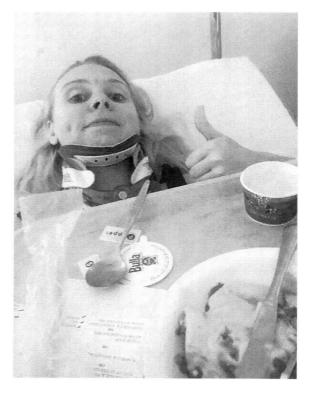

Visiting hours were filled with wonderful friends and church family. My table was lavished with food, mostly chocolate. People make everything worthwhile. Every trial can be overcome when you know you are loved. Unfortunately, I couldn't reach the food most of the time. The nurses brought my lunch and dinner but left it on the table in front of me without offering help to eat it. I made every effort to laugh at the situation while flat on my back, but nonetheless I felt very hungry.

Night-time was impossible. My bed was by a brightly lit doorway with a very loud bell that went off regularly. I assumed it was for patients in other wards needing assistance, but it meant no sleep for me. The poor man in the bed beside me was obviously in a lot of pain throughout the day. He would yell out sometimes, also throughout the night and in his sleep. I couldn't look at him, so I was never completely sure if he was asleep. One night I was lying there awake and he suddenly yelled in an angry voice, "Gonna kill her! Cut her up!" I have to say, at that point I was glad that I knew he was unable to get out of his bed.

On day three came a third MRI. I was so happy to finally be allowed to sit up straight in order to go there. As I lay on the machine bed, the doctor looked at me and said, "I recognise you." Yes, I was becoming quite the regular. It was a full spinal scan this time, so I was fully inside the loud machine and with a neck brace on. No light at the end of the tunnel. I remember thinking that I wasn't going to make it through. The last two MRIs had been OK; I had got through those without any problems. But this time I felt the internal choking of claustrophobia, with the brace around my neck. Everything felt too close, I was unable to move and breathing felt like much harder work. I held on tightly to the emergency button that they placed in my hand. I could press it if I needed to stop. In fact, at one point I was just moments away from pressing it; then suddenly the music started playing in the headphones. I shut my eyes, breathed in and began to relax.

Later that day, I was released to go home. I had to keep the neck brace on for another month, which was fine by me, as long as I could go home. The hospital gave me no information but booked me into an appointment with an orthopaedic surgeon. All I knew was that this was the bone doctor, which sounded like the right person to see.

Leah-Maarit Jeffery
July 30, 2013 · Cairns, QLD, Australia · 🌐 ▾

So far this year 14 X-rays, 1 CT and about to have a third MRI... I'm all scanned out!

A friend accompanied me to the doctor. I had my neck brace taken off and was told ever so candidly that their intention would be to do surgery on my neck, which involved putting a number of bolts into the bones of my neck. The doctor handed me a model neck structure, pointing out where the bolts would need to be placed. This would probably mean I would permanently lack full range of motion. Also, the doctor told me that it was a dangerous surgery so there would be risk of hitting an artery. My heart sank, but I held myself together, absorbing the information I was being presented with.

I was left with that and asked to come back a couple of weeks later. For the next two weeks, I was at my lowest point. In the evenings I would spend time listening to worship music but felt completely empty of fight. I felt so helpless. I was scared, but I had no options before me. Perhaps it seems dramatic, but I considered the possibility that perhaps I would die in the surgery that lay ahead of me. I still didn't actually have any answers as to why this was all happening to me.

One evening, I sat on the floor, feeling my absolute lowest. All options had been exhausted. I don't know what happened, but while I was sat there, I was suddenly filled with joy. I cannot explain it, but I started laughing and thanking God. It was the most unjustified joy that I had ever experienced.

There is a verse in the Bible that says, "Do not grieve, for the joy of the Lord is your strength."[1] I knew it well, but now for the first time I really understood it.

Leah-Maarit Jeffery
August 14, 2013 · Cairns, QLD, Australia · ⓖ ▼   ...

"Even when it hurts. Even when it's hard. Even when it all just falls apart.

I will run to you, 'cause I know that you are lover of my soul,

healer of my scars. You steady my heart!"

A few days later I went back to the doctor for the fateful next appointment. He told me that he had spoken to some other orthopaedic surgeons for a second opinion. *Good,* I thought. He then proceeded to say that they thought the surgery would be too dangerous to do, so they didn't want to do it. I said, "OK," and asked what he had in mind to do instead. The surgeon gave me a waffling response and suggested that I go to a physiotherapist for help. *A physiotherapist...? A physio...? Again?* For the first time in two years, I lost my patience with a doctor. I explained exactly why that was a bad idea and demanded that I have more blood tests done.

I'm not sure why I asked for blood tests again. I wasn't even sure what I was asking them to check for, as I knew I had had blood tests taken two years previously. Perhaps someone had suggested it. But I knew in my gut that this was the only thing left to do, as the doctors had exhausted their options. For this reason also, I was led to decide that if I couldn't get answers in Australia, then maybe I could get them back home in England. I spoke with my parents back in the UK and they agreed that it would be the right thing to do. My mum decided that she would fly to Australia and help to bring me back. After all, I was hardly able to walk, and I needed to pack up five years of belongings and furniture.

---

[1] Nehemiah 8:10

I began to sell off my bits and pieces, with a couple of months to get organised. I handed in my notice at work. It was very sad but also a relief. They were all very understanding. My last weeks at work were probably my most memorable and amusing, as for one month I continued working in my neck brace and began to enjoy the reactions from customers.

Leah-Maarit Jeffery ···
July 31, 2013 · Cairns, QLD, Australia · 🌏 ▾

Delivery man: Ohh *concerned face* ... What happened to you?

Me: Oh right, haha yeah ... I fought a kangaroo.

Delivery man: Oh! ... *concerned face" ... True!?

Me: Ummm ... Well no ... That was a joke.

Awkward silence

Leah-Maarit Jeffery ···
August 20, 2013 · Cairns, QLD, Australia · 🌏 ▾

I'm taking a survey of assumptions at Expressway Signs...

Apparently 'car accident' is the most common assumption of a person in a neck brace, with 'falling off a horse' coming in close second.

Leah-Maarit Jeffery ···
September 11, 2013 · Cairns, QLD, Australia · 🌏 ▾

Client: What happened to you? You look like a zombie.

Me thinking: You need to leave now...

I was at the point where I was unable to drive so was relying on lifts, taxis and home deliveries. With Mum there to help on the last week, everything became easier. I distinctly remember going swimming together one day and shed a few tears when I realised I could no longer kick my legs to swim at all. I wondered if I would ever be able to swim again. It was something I loved to do.

My church family threw me an Australia-themed leaving party, bigger than I could have imagined. The whole church came, and more. There was live entertainment from different friends, a photo reel, presents, Australia-themed games such as 'throw the thong[2]', and kangaroo steak

---

[2] flip-flop

burgers being handed around the room. I dressed as Olivia Newton John (Sandy), while others dressed as other Australian-themed characters. I was so blessed by it. My only regret was that I couldn't enjoy and appreciate it in the way that I would have wanted to because of the exhaustion I felt. I also regret not being able to fully thank all the people that cared for me over this time in the way that I wanted to. But I hope that they know that I did not take one act of kindness for granted in my heart, even if I was unable to repay it. Leaving Australia was leaving everything that I had worked for over the previous five years: leaving work, friends, church, my home, furniture, clothes and belongings. This was not my Plan A. This was not even my Plan B. This was not my plan at all.

A song that stuck with me over this last year in Australia, with words which were both equally challenging and comforting, was 'Oceans' by Hillsong. We sang it quite regularly and it resonated in my heart.

You call me out upon the waters
The great unknown where feet may fail
And there I find You in the mystery
In oceans deep
My faith will stand
I will call upon Your name
And keep my eyes above the waves
When oceans rise, my soul will rest in Your embrace
For I am Yours and You are mine
Your grace abounds in deepest waters
Your sovereign hand
Will be my guide
Where feet may fail and fear surrounds me
You've never failed and You won't start now
Spirit, lead me where my trust is without borders
Let me walk upon the waters
Wherever You would call me
Take me deeper than my feet could ever wander
And my faith will be made stronger
In the presence of my Saviour

I made my final trip back to the doctor. The blood test results indicated that I was anaemic (no surprises there, as I had no hunger or enjoyment in eating anything) but also showed something else. I didn't know what it meant, but finally something was telling the doctors that things were not normal. He said he would give me the results to take back to the UK.

3

Mother Land

My mum and I got to the airport. She insisted that I wore my neck brace when we got on the plane so that people would give me some space. It was a good idea, even though I felt like a fraud, not needing it anymore. I felt nervous about how I would manage on the long-haul flight. Normally, just an hour sitting down caused my hip to seize up and be very stiff and painful.

The first leg of the flight was about thirteen hours or so, to Hong Kong. We made it. I managed to get off the plane. Then all flights to London were ushered in one direction, following a Chinese man who seemed to be in quite a hurry. He rushed everyone along. I limped along as fast as I could, as my stiff leg tried to come back to life. My mum called out to the man, asking him to slow down for my sake. I could see that he was torn, as he tried to slow down but really wasn't able to.

We eventually got through to the waiting lounge in the correct terminal for our next flight with some hours left to kill. I desperately needed to lie down to give my neck relief. It was by this point quite normal for me to need to rest my neck every twenty minutes at least, to relieve the ache and pain. We found a spot where I could lie on the floor. I wasn't sure if I would be able to get up again though. After I had lain there in agony and discomfort for a while, Mum managed to help me up; I definitely would not have been able to do it without her help.

Eventually we were back on English soil. Settling back into UK life felt quite pleasant. I was finally able to rest and was fully looked after. This was what I needed, but it didn't come without frustrations. I had spent the last two years dealing with this and 'getting on with it', and now I had people telling me to *stop* doing things. I didn't like the idea of ever becoming helpless and if I could do it, I wanted to do it. After all, I didn't know how long it would be until I could never do these things anymore. My family would rush to pick things up for me that I dropped, and open doors for me, and get me food. I wasn't used to this. In fact, it became an annoyance to me. I realised this was going to be my next life lesson.

Time went on and I learnt to accept people helping me, even if it still grated me a little on the inside. This was why I was here. *To heal.*

A few times the question arose from people, "Do you think you will get a wheelchair soon?"

"No!" would be my sudden retort, in disbelief that they would even suggest it. But the truth was, I fantasised about it. The relief of getting around in a chair on wheels actually sounded amazing, even though I fought against the idea of it actually happening.

We went to see the local UK doctor and repeated the blood tests, two more MRI scans and everything else that had been done before. I was nervous for these fourth and fifth MRIs, given how I'd felt the previous time. This time they injected me with some kind of dye. Then they put the headphones on and I entered the tunnel. I felt my heart begin to race a little as the loud noises began whirring on repeat. *Where was the music? Had they forgotten to switch it on?* I needed the music.

After what was probably ten minutes, and I was completely tense, I suddenly heard the first few notes of music flood through my ears. It was Coldplay; the track I had been listening to for the whole week on repeat, making me feel at ease. The song is called *Trouble*. As it started playing, I felt every muscle relax and the tension fall out of my body. (I am quite surprised that I don't glow with the amount of radiation I must have had over the last few years!)

Next, I was booked in to see a rheumatologist. *A rheumatologist? Well, that's different. Surely that's a positive sign...* I was right. It *was* positive. I sat with my mum in front of another seemingly abrupt doctor, but despite her abruptness, I could tell that she was good. She was clear, to the point, a no-nonsense kind of doctor. I didn't mind that. She explained to me that the tests had come back with a result, that I had something called *ankylosing spondylitis.*

I never thought I'd feel so relieved to be told that I had an incurable disease. But I did, because I finally had an answer. It sat right with me this time. It made sense.

As the rheumatologist talked through what this was and assured me that I now had options, I knew a corner was about to be turned. She explained that in my case the condition was aggressive and so the damage done in my hip over two years would usually have taken twenty years in other people with AS. I was already living with what she called "an eighty-year-old hip". Well, that certainly explained a lot...

Before I continue, I would like to make something clear. As soon as I had got back to the UK, I had started to feel better in myself, way before the diagnosis and before any treatment had begun. It was long after I read back my diary excerpt, about the eagle flying me off the ground and into the sunset, that I was reminded about this time. God knew it would take trust in him; leaving my familiar surroundings behind, in order to have the peace and perspective that was waiting for me.

Isaiah 40:31 says,

> *...but those who hope in the LORD*
> *will renew their strength.*
> *They will soar on wings like eagles;*
> *they will run and not grow weary,*
> *they will walk and not be faint.*

When no one can tell you what's wrong with you, no matter how obvious it is that there's a problem, you can still feel that perhaps you are making it up or it's not as bad as you think it is. Pain is not normal. Pain is not something to just put up with without answers.

I found myself thinking, "I'm willing to do anything, just as long as I don't have to give myself an injection." The doctor then proceeded to explain about a drug called Humira, which I would need to give myself as a fortnightly injection, if we were able to get approval for it. Oh dear... They do not give it to everyone as it is too expensive, but she was confident I would qualify. She gave me a steroid injection for some temporary pain relief. She was not gentle. She jabbed that needle in my 'booty' and I nearly passed out. However, it was worth it. I felt better for a few weeks. I also got my appetite back. I went from picking at food that I didn't really want, to eating a large plateful, going back for seconds and pudding every mealtime. That food made me so happy and suddenly seemed to taste so good. So, I got a bit overweight for a season. Oh well!

After some weeks and more tests, I was finally approved for this new drug. I was shocked to be told that each injection would cost the NHS around £400. When they delivered my first box of four, I couldn't get my head around the fact that there was £1,600 worth of medication in my fridge. A nurse came to my house to 'show me the ropes'. She brought with her a yellow sharps box to throw away the used needles, a friendly welcome pack (as though I'd just joined some elite club) and, of course, the dreaded needle. She walked me through it very slowly and I was grateful that she made me feel so at ease. I managed to inject myself and was surprised because it wasn't that bad. Thank goodness the needle was smaller than I expected it to be! So that was that. I was then on my own, and the next few weeks would be a waiting game to see if the drug worked.

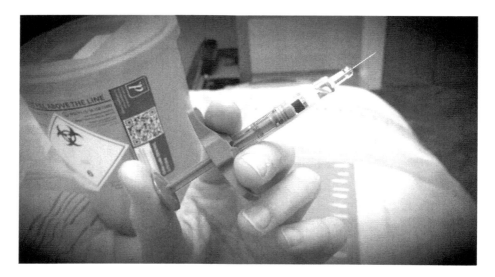

I am quite sure I started feeling better even in the first week. I started being able to climb the stairs quicker. Some weeks passed, and I was soon cheering and feeling very proud because I managed to sit down on the floor by myself. I began taking a walk around the block once a day. It was hard work at first as my limp left me exhausted after a few minutes, but every few days I noticed small improvements. I don't remember how many weeks or months had passed, but during one walk I reached an alleyway about twenty metres long and I sprinted along it as fast as my legs could possibly take me. This was the first time I had run in a long time and I felt like I'd just won gold at the Olympics. Another day I went swimming with my mum – the first time since leaving Australia. I kicked my legs and splashed like a dog, desperately trying to stay afloat for five metres, swimming into my mum's arms. It was like a mother and toddler moment, learning to swim… except I was a five-foot-seven toddler.

Leah-Maarit Jeffery
July 3, 2014 · ⊙ ▾

Today I ran as fast as I could.... just for a minute.... but it felt good

Over this time, I reconnected with my old school friend whom I had lost touch with during my time in Australia. It felt like no time had passed at all. We planned days out and she gave a lot of time to me, which I appreciated immensely. She also had been doing some personal training on the side of her main job. We decided that in the New Year we would begin training together. This was over a year since I had been back in the UK. She gave me free sessions, and although I had never done anything like it, I loved it. Our first time was on New Year's Day – a cold, frosty morning. She packed all her training gear into her little silver Ford Fiesta and we drove to the local park near her house in Crawley. Laying out all these unfamiliar things onto the field, we began the torture. She hit me hard with burpees, mountain climbers, battle ropes, weights and other things I'd never heard of until that day. I was finally starting to feel like myself. I had regained a lot of my energy and movement, and I kept saying that I felt human again. The range of motion in my neck and hip improved but was still limited. The most noticeable improvement was that the pain finally started to go away.

My rheumatologist told me all about the fantastic English charity organisation called NASS (National Ankylosing Spondylitis Society). They have a website full of resources,[3] and I also got hold of their book which is filled with simple daily stretches and exercises to help people with AS. I wanted to learn everything I possibly could about this. I wanted to know exactly what was going on in my body. The hardest thing to learn was how to pronounce it.

The daily NASS exercises had begun before my time on the field. I enjoyed doing these. They helped me take note of the progress I was making, as week by week things became easier. The difficult part was that as I began to do and achieve more things throughout my day, the priority level of exercises gradually became less important. I needed to

---

[3] *www.nass.co.uk*

learn to mix up the exercises in order to keep it interesting, challenging and important to me.

It's about time I actually explained what AS is. This will not be a science lesson because, quite frankly, I'm the creative type and science, however interesting, is not my fountain of knowledge. I will do my best to keep this relatively simple but informative. Firstly, AS is an autoimmune disease. That simply means that my immune system is so effective, it not only kills off the bad guys but it starts attacking the good guys too. That covers a whole lot of diseases, so let me narrow it down some more. AS is a bit like arthritis that mostly affects the spine (but can affect other joints and ligaments). The spine includes the neck and hips. The naughty overactive immune system decides to start attacking joints in the spine, which causes inflammation to occur. This inflammation causes all the pain and stiffness, and over time creates what is called 'calcification' around the bones (I'm allowed one fancy word). Put simply, this means that extra bone grows where the joints should be. So the spine of a person with AS may eventually fuse together and become hunched forward. That's why someone with AS should always work on their posture and flexibility. A certain physiotherapist that I saw once said to me, "You must work on your posture so that you are upright when your bones fuse together," then quickly corrected herself, "*If* they fuse." I could tell that she assumed it was inevitable, even if she wasn't supposed to say it.

There are other common issues that latch onto AS, such as psoriasis (skin problems), uveitis (eye problems), Crohn's disease (gut problems), rib cage inflammation (lung problems) and other lesser common things. I am grateful to not have any of these, however I am quite sure that fatigue is part of every AS warrior's journey. I do experience fatigue and what's known as 'brain fog'.

The hardest thing about tiredness/fatigue is not knowing when it is AS-related and when it is just me being lazy or 'regular tired'. Because honestly, I still can't tell the difference. I can be lazy. I am human. I am working on it. If I am tired because of the AS, I should be able to allow myself some extra rest and be able to say no to things without self-doubt. However, if I am tired just like anyone else gets tired, I should be able to push through and get on with it, without a backlash of exhaustion the next day. I have a friend who has suffered with cystic fibrosis her whole life; she said that she feels exactly the same way.

On the other hand, I think brain fog is worse. I don't know if it is really the same thing for everyone, but for me it is when my thoughts just turn into a haze, and the ability to concentrate or bring focus to my thoughts feels like extremely hard work, if not impossible. As a graphic designer, I am prone to this if I am tired and in front of my computer screen. I don't think the screen light helps at all. I have no doubt that most people can feel this way when they are working. I am simply convinced that it happens to me on a more regular basis. It makes me feel stupid. I can be hard on myself when my head empties. I tend to over-compensate by talking more, and then realising that my words are making very little sense, or just not at all what I want to be saying. A good example of this happened this week. My teenage niece was asking some questions on important life matters. I felt it desperately important to answer her well, yet my words came out in an overflowing spillage of mumbo-jumbo-tosh. As I dropped her home, my heart sank, as I felt the weight of a failed aunty moment. I sat straight down at my computer and wrote her the words I had meant to say. Writing it down seemed to come a whole lot more naturally.

When I first found out about AS, I was given the impression that it was relatively rare. Perhaps it is. I read in some places that 0.2% of the population have it. Other places tell me that it's 2%. I believe that it's more than we think. One thing is for sure: for a long time, not enough has been understood about this condition, and it is most often misdiagnosed for years beforehand. On average it can take seven to ten years to be diagnosed correctly, as this is how long it takes for the changes in the specific (sacroiliac) joints to show up on a regular X-ray. To me, that is unbelievable. My two years felt like a lifetime, but the aggressiveness of my condition at least led to answers faster than most people with AS can hope for.

Spending time with my friend, the physical accomplishments began to stack up. We took trips to Scotland and Wales, going for mountainous hikes and adventures. Not only did I enjoy the fact that I could do these things, it had also been a long time since I'd been able to enjoy the sheer beauty of the UK landscape. Cairns is stunningly beautiful, but with the abundance of dangerous creatures, you cannot truly experience the land in the same way that you can in England. Unless you are stupid or fearless. I am neither.

It didn't take me long to start thinking about what I was going to do for work. I wasn't ready to get back into a full-time job. I knew that my resting season was just beginning. However, I needed some form of income. It was incredibly helpful living at home and having the opportunity to consider working for myself as a freelance graphic designer. I began using my time to develop some business ideas, working on my brand, my website and a portfolio. I placed an advert in a local magazine and posted flyers around wherever possible. I had enough savings to keep me going for a few months at least. These ventures didn't amount to much more than the odd job here and there. However, I eventually landed some freelance work at a sign company in Surrey. They worked in a similar fashion to my previous company, but without any customer interaction. Purely design layouts. The work was very sporadic, giving me some very busy months and fantastic money, and other months of nothing at all. This way of life was perfect for me, as I was finding my way back on my feet and continuing to make the most of the rest.

The year after my diagnosis, I took a trip back to Australia. I felt prepared in my heart that everyone may have moved on and things would have changed during my time away. That wasn't so. It felt as though no time has passed and I had never left there. I loved that people were able to see how much better I was, walking more normally and even swimming again. It was a lovely time, but I knew it was only temporary. I only had enough injections supplied to me to last the weeks that I was there. So despite the extremely generous offer from the church to buy me another return flight to extend my stay, I was unable to accept. That's when I realised that I was tied. I could only go where and for how long the injections allowed. They needed to be kept at fridge temperature at all times, so long-haul flights with medication was in itself a challenge. As I headed home to the UK to continue the journey I was on, it dawned on me that my heart for travel was now walled in somewhat.

Not a lot changed over the next two years. Work continued with its highs and lows. I continued enjoying my new gym membership. I found great comfort from a few very active Facebook pages for people with AS. These forums are excellent places to share, to ask questions, to be sad sometimes and to celebrate at other times.

I began doing something I never thought I would ever want to do. I started to run. It started out as a social thing. My friend and I would go for long jogs together while chatting about life. We would get so far and then become quite silent, just willing ourselves to the end. I realised that although it was tough, I really enjoyed the challenge of seeing how far I could go. I was only a beginner and not nearly as competitive as some, but my friend convinced me that we should sign up for the Reigate Half Marathon in Surrey. It was a great idea, even though I had only been used to running 5km. We ran more regularly together, and one day we even managed 13km, but as the time drew closer, my energy levels and motivation began to drop fast. I don't know if it was a spell of fatigue, psychological, or simply the summer heat kicking in, but I struggled. On top of that, my knee started to hurt. As soon as the knee pains became a regular thing, I decided to quit. Yes. *I quit.* I decided it wasn't worth damaging my knee.

You might wonder why I shared that story, given that we never achieved the half-marathon. The point is, that whole process was a breakthrough for me. Running 13km was a huge achievement I never thought I would have the chance or ability to do. As a consolation we later took to a 5km Colour Run at Hever Castle. It was so much fun. It was a beautiful foggy day and we ran around the castle grounds with bombs of colour powder being thrown at every stretch. Someone had gone around the statues placing 'cheeky' coloured handprints onto the statues' bottoms. I don't know what was in that colour powder but I couldn't stop laughing all afternoon.

After almost two-and-a-half years in Surrey, I moved with my parents, brother and nieces to Exeter. It was a completely new start for all of us. I had strongly considered moving back to Australia, having been offered a full-time job, but in an extremely last-minute decision, I felt that Exeter was the right destination for me.

4

Scalpel-Ready

I finally felt ready to take the plunge and go back into full-time work, putting the freelancing on hold. In the weeks leading up to the move, I was offered an interview at another sign company as a sign maker. This was not a graphic design job; it involved a little design set-up work but was more of a practical job. It required working the printers, cutting materials, putting prints onto signs – physically making what needed to be made. Why did I go for this job? Well, firstly, I simply wanted to. I had always loved the idea of doing something practical, but I had never learnt the skills. I dreamt of being a builder, but I'm ashamed to admit that the challenges of being both inexperienced and female felt too much for me. I knew I had all the head knowledge of a sign-maker, just not the experience. Secondly, I went for this job because of my AS. Exercise is good for keeping your joints flexible and minimising stiffness and unwanted bone growth. So, in my mind, working at a desk all day was not going to help me in the long run. Sitting at a desk is easier on the tiredness levels, but in the long run I couldn't see it being the best solution for my lifestyle.

I got the job, but I was on the bottom rung; I had no practical experience and the guys (plus one girl) I was working with all had a few years of experience at least. It was easy for them. But I was challenged. I wasn't used to having a scalpel knife in my hand all day, which inevitably led to excessive finger cuts. It turned out I was pretty clumsy. OK, I had always known this, but anyone can improve with practice. "Happens to everyone at the beginning," they reassured me. The fact is, I knew I wasn't good yet. It was a challenge to my pride, having been in a previous position where I was good at my job and highly appreciated, to now be much the opposite. Now everything was about learning. I was determined to keep going, even when I felt a failure. Ultimately, the job was fun, and everything I learnt was a step forward. I didn't plan to go back to the old.

No longer than a couple of months in, I started noticing hip pains at the end of the day at work. I didn't think much of it at first; they were long days and my body was working harder than usual. Of course I would expect some aches and pains... Only, they didn't go away. I noticed that they began to get worse and came more frequently. I just kept getting on with it. I couldn't afford to overthink anything. As the months went on, on some days the pain was excruciating. I never told anyone too much detail of my condition, because I had told them at my initial interview that I was "doing loads better" and nothing was going to get in the way of my working.

The limp usually returned after lunchtime at first. On one hand, I didn't want to talk about it because of fear of losing the job (I was on an extended initial contract), but on the other hand, I was surprised that no one ever mentioned anything when I was so obviously limping. At least I assumed it was obvious, although I was doing my utmost for it not to be. I never got asked, "What's wrong with your leg?" Maybe it's a British thing. In Australia every customer that walked through the door would ask me what was wrong with me. I think I prefer being asked, but I have heard from many people with physical conditions that they don't like talking about it to people and that it's none of their business. As is usually the way in life, people are different and there's not a one-size-fits-all way to show care and compassion. Sometimes love takes trial and error. However much the risk of error, never stop trialling.

After six months of working, I went to my new rheumatologist in Exeter. I explained how I felt and he took a new X-ray (working on my glow). It showed that my right hip had got worse since I had arrived back in the UK and that my cartilage had almost completely eroded. He said that I had three choices. Number one would be to leave it. It would be painful but I wouldn't die from it. Number two would be to have a steroid injection for pain relief to see if it helped for a little while. Number three would be to have a hip replacement. He then recommended number three, but I think he wanted to reassure me that it was all down to my choice. I was relieved. This hip had been causing me trouble for four years by this point and it was crystal clear that it wasn't going to get better on its own accord. The downside was that it would take six months on the waiting list before surgery could be performed. I would also need to see the orthopaedic surgeon who would need to confirm that he agreed to do the surgery. A few weeks later I saw him. He seemed relatively young, but I had been assured that he was fantastic. That was it. I was on the list.

Another waiting game. It seemed too long. I looked into the possibility of surgery through private healthcare, but the operation would cost £12,000, which was more than half my annual wage at the time. I agreed to work for another three months, but after two I realised that I just couldn't do it. I was concerned that there would come a day very soon when I wouldn't be able to drive home. It was already feeling dangerous at times, having a seized-up leg on the accelerator. So I quit my job and went back to freelance design. I had battled internally about that decision for weeks. I knew it would be a long time without work before and after surgery, so it didn't seem like the wise choice. But I was the only one who really knew how I was physically feeling. No one else could give me better advice, no matter how much I asked. I then felt a peace about finishing early. I knew that I would manage and God would provide for me, even if it meant writing off all my plans for the year. And yes, it did mean that. My plans would have been written off anyway, with the way things were, whether I was working or not.

The next few months seemed to pass very slowly. It was a rather frustrating wait, as I wouldn't be given a surgery date until possibly a few weeks beforehand. The surgery would mean needing to stop injections for a few weeks also, and it was unknown how that would make me feel at that point. Eventually, in May, I received my appointment for 'Pre-op'. This is a standard appointment in which they perform a number of simple tests and ask questions, to ensure that you are prepared not only physically for the surgery, but also practically afterwards. I left with a small shopping list (and prescription) for items such as a couple of toilet frames, an appropriately heighted chair, a reaching tool, and various other bits and pieces. The reaching tool certainly became my favourite. I rather enjoyed practising how independent I could manage to be with my 'reacher', and how many unsuspecting people I could poke in the process.

Leading up to the surgery, I spent many days reading through my information booklet supplied by the hospital. I scanned through article after article online of people's experiences with hip replacements. I looked at gruesome photographs but couldn't bring myself to watch a video. I wanted to be informed but not freaked out. A friend of mine told me the story of when she did work experience with a doctor which involved sitting in on a live hip replacement. She recalled as they made the incision and then used an electrothermal device which heats and seals the tissue from bleeding. She had a moment where she thought happily, "Mmm, smells delicious... like steak," and then it dawned on her. "Oh no! That's a human!" It's funny to think of the things you don't consider.

All in all, I was surprisingly calm about what was going to happen. There was no point being worried, in my mind. It was going to happen, it would go well, and I would feel normal again by the following year. It wasn't until a week before surgery that unexpected feelings crept up on me. I can't easily explain my emotion, except to say that I felt nothing. A wave of 'emptiness' seemed to come over me; I felt I didn't care about anything and didn't want to see anyone or do anything. I wanted to avoid everyone. The underlying sense was perhaps that I had been waiting so long and now I just needed to get on with it. I also felt afraid of the helplessness that was about to follow: going back to being waited on hand and foot, without the independence that I revel in. Even as I write this, I find myself asking questions. *Why do I so revel in my independence? Is that wrong? Is that right? Is that how God made us to be?* I think it is how our nature has caused us to be, over and over again throughout history; we are sure that we can handle it all ourselves. We're eager to say, "I did this by my own strength." I don't believe that is the way we should be or need to be, despite living in a world that tells us otherwise. I believe that we have been made for community and that God wants to carry the load in our weaknesses. He wants us to look to him to help. He wants to be involved in our struggles.

The day of surgery arrived. My brother drove me to the hospital and spent a number of hours sitting and waiting with me while I was gowned up and prepared. Despite the many hours of waiting, it felt very sudden when a young nurse finally collected me and whisked me only a few metres down the hall, where through a set of double doors stood my surgery bed and two friendly anaesthetists. In the months leading up to surgery, one of the decisions I had needed to make was which form of anaesthetic I would like. A spinal anaesthetic would involve having the drug injected into my spine, which could result in me being slightly conscious but very sleepy. The other alternative would be a general anaesthetic with which I would be completely asleep but with a much higher chance of vomiting and feeling nauseous afterwards, and a longer recovery time. After much deliberation and advice, I decided to go for the spinal but asked if they could make me a bit sleepier if possible. I sat on the edge of the bed as a young nurse asked me some light-hearted questions about where I lived. The doctor gave me the spinal injection which, I am relieved to say, did not hurt any more than a regular injection. They put a needle into a vein in my hand and connected it to what I assume was the general anaesthetic. I was talking to the doctor, then halfway through the sentence said, "Woah, OK... I'm starting to feel that," giggling as my brain worked overtime to piece my sentence together. That's the last I remember of the next few hours.

When I came to, I was lying on a bed in a large room full of other beds and a couple of nurses. I have no recollection of real time at this point, but I remember being aware that I was waiting for a while before they took me off to the ward. I lay there, curious by the numb weightiness of my legs. I stared at my feet, willing my toes to move. My left toes (the non-operated leg) wiggled as usual. The right leg, however, did not. Then suddenly my toes threw themselves upwards. It was a strange sensation as it wasn't quite what my brain was telling them to do and I couldn't feel the movement at all. It was as if they were detached from my body. I felt pleasantly surprised at the fact that I felt quite OK. Perhaps it was the relief that it was done and I was out the other end.

They wheeled me to the ward, which was also a fairly large room with eleven other beds. All the ladies who shared the ward were elderly, except for a couple of women who were probably no more than ten years older than me.

I had felt right to move to Exeter, and it turned out that Exeter Hospital has a world-renowned team of specialist hip consultants. I had been told how good the surgeons and care were at the hospital for those undergoing hip replacements, so I knew I would be getting the best possible care.

I spent the first night struggling to sleep, as a nurse came around fairly regularly taking my blood pressure. Each time it was too low, so she kept asking me to drink more water. I drank and drank, yet it never seemed to improve. I just kept drinking every time that the nurse told me to. Then, at about 3am, another nurse plugged me into a machine through the needle in my hand. I assume she was injecting me with more morphine, but I'm still not absolutely sure.

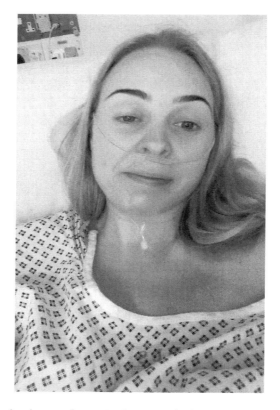

I probably had two hours' sleep and then morning arrived. I felt hopeful that recovery would be quick, given my young age of thirty-one and having chosen the spinal anaesthetic. I had been told that they would do their best to get patients out of bed and on their feet the next day if they were able to. It felt nice to be able to simply sit up, given my previous hospital experience in Australia.

After a fairly challenging and sleep-deprived night, I didn't feel great and was also very aware that I needed the toilet. We were told that the physiotherapists would come around mid-morning and see one patient at a time, in no particular order; when they arrived, they could get me out of bed and hopefully to the toilet. One thing I learnt while in the hospital in Australia was that I cannot use a bed pan. It does not matter how desperately I need to go, my body just won't allow it. However, that was my only choice. I explained this to the nurses, yet willingly agreed to try. But no. Not the first time. Not the second time. Not the third, fourth or fifth time. "Where are those physios?" I whined. They were late this time. No one had an answer as to when they would arrive. I became more and more uncomfortable, to the point that I was extremely frustrated as none of the nurses seemed to understand the urgency of how I felt. Everyone has experienced that kind of pain. Eventually, the physios started turning up, two by two, visiting other patients' beds and going through their routine of getting them up. I felt desperate for their arrival, however then two other young men walked in with an empty bed. They were there to take me to have my post-op X-ray. I could not force a smile for them. I was ready to cry with frustration. I did not have time for this. I just about held it together as they slid me onto the bed, took me off to have the X-ray and brought me back afterwards.

Finally, two ladies arrived in burgundy scrubs, heading towards me. *The physios. Finally!* They drew my curtains and slowly sat me up. They talked me through a few things, adjusted my new elbow crutches to the correct height and checked if I could move my legs. My operated leg felt like a heavy weight, but I managed to move my legs off the side of the bed. As they eventually got me to stand to my feet, not three seconds later I felt dizziness kick in...

"Leah... Leah..." My name was being repeated, in darkness. My vision returned, and my eyes widened with the two unknown faces up close to me. *Who are they? What's going on?* My eyes stared hard, switching between the two, my thoughts racing to catch up. A few moments later I remembered where I was and what had happened. I had blacked out and fallen diagonally back onto the bed. I internally panicked for a moment at the thought that I had fallen, as my hip was in an extremely fragile state. They put me back into bed properly and said they would need to try again tomorrow.

'Oh no!' I thought, thoroughly frustrated again. I still needed the toilet and I was feeling awful. The physios walked off and a nurse came in through the curtains. I explained again how I felt. She could see that something needed to be done. She walked out for a moment and as she did, I suddenly felt a sickness come over me. I knew what that meant. I scanned the table next to me and reached for an empty bag lying there. I was very sick. *A lot* sick. But, needless to say, I felt instantly better. The nurse returned as I shamefully, yet feeling relieved, handed her the bag. I was determined I would be able to get up now. The truth is, I wasn't sure at all, but I couldn't possibly wait another twenty-four hours.

They weren't going to bring the physios back to get me onto crutches, but they were able to bring the portable wheelchair-style toilet to me, which involved me standing for two seconds as I migrated to the chair. I felt extremely fragile and nervous, but managed it. I was since repeatedly congratulated by nurses on my 'bladder of steel'.

For the whole morning, I had been well aware that I would be having visitors arrive in the early afternoon. I had known that I wouldn't be able to face anyone feeling the way that I had. But with the drama of the morning behind me, half an hour passed and then my first lovely visitor showed up. I quickly returned to feeling normal again (as normal as could be expected). I felt so relieved to see familiar and caring faces. I relayed some of my morning events, feeling unsure if they could believe me, given the smiling, seemingly relaxed girl in front of them.

The next night was also fairly restless, but I managed a few more hours of sleep. Compression pumps had been wrapped around my legs to keep my circulation flowing well, which made irregular noises throughout the night. Eventually I got used to this. A dear old lady in the bed opposite was the main culprit of the lack of sleep. I am quite sure she had Alzheimer's and regularly called out to the nurses for help, as she was confused about where she was and where the toilet was. She wasn't allowed out of bed, as she had just had a hip operation also, and the nurses would come and explain this to her every fifteen minutes or so. It was interesting to see the different approaches of the nurses. Some would be kind and patient with her, no matter how many times they repeated themselves. Others would talk to her like a child needing reprimanding and ignore her calling out until she had got herself half out of bed.

The third day was much easier than the previous. The morning began with waiting for the physios to come and do their rounds. I was not feeling rushed this time, nonetheless I was still extremely keen to get out of bed. The next time that I called the nurse for the 'toilet chair', she suggested we would try getting up again properly. I sat up and slowly slid my legs off the bedside. I wanted to sit and wait. I still felt extremely light-headed, but not dizzy this time. I was not going to rush this now. I felt very afraid of the possibility of passing out onto the floor and dislocating my hip. A little while of sitting passed and I was ready. Holding onto the crutches, I lifted myself up, the way that I was shown. *I was up.* Who knew that standing could be so nerve-wracking? As slowly as a tortoise, I carefully took secure, calculated steps forward. The bathroom was only five metres away. I made it there. Then I made it back. *Success!* I felt exhausted. It was then straight back onto the bed for a lie down. One thing I did not expect while I was at the hospital was the tiredness that came with it. Even sitting up straight would be a tiring activity that I could only do for short stints of time.

A steady flow of visitors continued to come from early afternoon to evening, with a couple of hours' break in the middle. My dear friends had arranged it this way; without me knowing, they had planned to take turns throughout visiting hours. I was really in need of the conversation, laughter and familiar faces. However, my energy levels came in sudden peaks and troughs.

The evening arrived, and I was quite determined to get a bit more sleep this time. I put my headphones on, purely to dampen some of the noise of the room. However, the ladies decided it would be a good time for a late-night chat, so I lay back listening in. The lady with Alzheimer's was trying to get out of bed again and calling out apologies to the nurses for, as she would say, "being a nuisance". A young nurse came to her aid and all the other patients, quite concerned for her, began asking her questions about her younger days. "I bet you never had to wear scruffy uniforms like we've got on," laughed the young nurse, tugging on her baggy scrubs. In not much time, the lady began to become far more responsive and coherent as she spoke about her time working as a nurse in the post-war period. She proudly spoke about her position and the details of her immaculate uniform. Her voice changed, and a confidence seemed to come over her as she recalled the details. It was quite amazing to hear this change in the lady that, up until this point, had seemed helpless and frustrated.

Day four arrived. Each day felt a little better. All that I needed now was to conquer the stairs, and then I would be allowed to go home. It was like the morning before your driving test. You have to pass the test, because if you don't you're going to have to reschedule and no one wants that wait. The morning passed with its usual routines of medication, food, new bedsheets and freshening up. A few of the women had gone home over the previous twenty-four hours, so the ward felt quieter on this day. Eventually two new physios came to me and brought a wheelchair along. They wheeled me down the hallway and to a flight of stairs. Here was the test. I felt fairly confident, and with their explanation of what to do and how to do it, I slowly made my way up. *I passed!* I turned and slid back down, one careful step at a time. Back to the ward.

After having been given the go ahead to go home later that day, there were only the practical things left to do. A young man came to remind me of all the precautions that I needed to take over the next six weeks: no crossing legs, no sitting on a chair lower than eighteen inches, no standing on my right leg with more than 50% pressure, no riding in a car. I would be effectively housebound for six weeks. Or at least I could only go as far as I could walk... which was not very far. With my patched-up wound, I was eager to see what was underneath, but it would be two more weeks until the nurses came around to remove the dressing.

The time came to leave. My family arrived to collect me. It was the one time I would be allowed in a car. I nervously got in. The chance of dislocation or infection is highest in the first six weeks and I was happy to keep to all the rules that I had been given over this time. As far I was concerned, breaking rules would definitely not be worth the risk, however restricted I felt.

5

My Battle Cry

The next couple of weeks were filled with regular lie downs, 'extreme' exercises like wiggling my toes, and a whole lot of sitting in the sunshine. The two weeks following the op were probably the best weather days of the whole year. Being mid-June and hot sunshine, I spent much of the time in the garden, under the shade of oak trees. I had a large number of DVD box sets waiting for me and various means of entertainment, but when it came to it, I was surprisingly happy with just sitting and being; listening intently to the different sounds of the birds and resting fully in the fact that I had no subconscious awareness of any work that I would need to get back to next month. "So, this is what retirement feels like," I smirked, while watching my mum pull out the weeds in the flowerbeds around me. Having said that, almost every day I would have a visitor or two, which my time seemed to focus around. I was overwhelmed by the love of all the people that came to see me. I imagined that after the hospital time was over, I wouldn't see friends much for a while. But it was quite the opposite. In fact, some days I had trouble scheduling in times for people to come. It was also a great blessing for my parents who were looking after me, as it meant that they could go out and have time to do what they needed to without worrying that I would be left alone.

Ten days in, two nurses arrived to change the dressing. This was my first look at the scar. I was surprised by how neat it was and the fact that is was only about six inches long. I had expected it to be bigger and more curved, based on photos that I had seen of others. The surgeon had done a fantastic job.

As the weeks crept on, I began to start testing out putting a little extra pressure onto my foot. It would feel like a pins and needles sensation shooting through my foot. The muscles and nerves were just beginning to come to life, having been cut through in the surgery.

Then came the day that I first took a couple of steps without crutches. My whole body felt like a heavy weight as I made the steps, but it was an exciting moment of progress. It was a very different experience to the progress I'd felt when I had come back from Australia. This progress came more naturally. Without the fight. In the day before my six-week check-up, the ability to walk came quickly. I was ready to go. I had stuck to the rules for six weeks as best as I could and now I was ready to throw the rules out of the window. This was a new season about to begin; a fresh chapter in my story.

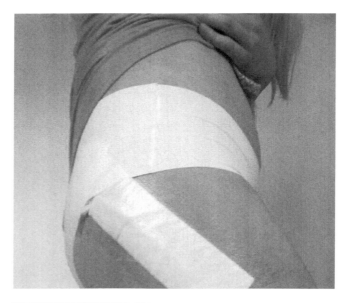

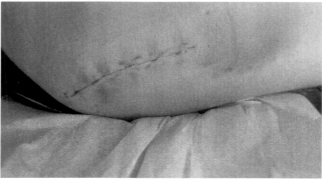

Returning to the hospital, I walked in without the crutches, but still with a limp, as expected. I met with another physio. It was the same girl who had been seeing me the time I had passed out onto the bed after surgery. I remembered her face and laughed a little awkwardly, insisting that I was not going to pass out this time. She listed the precautions that I no longer needed to worry about and then went on to confirm all the precautions that would be ongoing. *Forever.* It wasn't really until this point that it occurred to me that I would have some very basic limitations that would always be there; such as not being able to cross one leg over the other, no excessive twisting, no deep squatting (probably only relevant to my gym routine). This was a fairly quick review, and then I went on to see one of the surgeons. I had not seen this man before, although he told me a little more about the operation and assured me that it had all gone well and was successful. I was happy to get to see the X-ray of my shiny new hip. It was a strange sight, knowing that this piece of metal was now a part of me, but reassuring too.

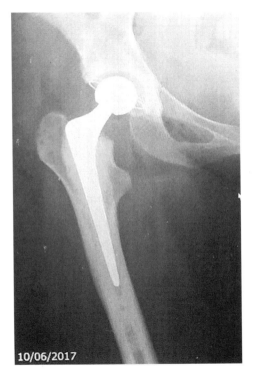

10/06/2017

Friends would often ask if I could feel the metal. I couldn't. Nothing felt different except for the fact that I could stand up tall and straight for the first time in years without my right knee bent forward. I could lie flat on my back, legs stretched out, in actual comfort. Every few days I would feel a different pain, which seemed to worry me every time. One time I raced down the stairs too fast and hurt my ankle. I worried that I may have damaged it badly, but it was just another part of the healing process. My leg had been stuck out at an angle for so long that my joints were not used to the idea of beginning to straighten up.

Following this appointment, I was booked in to see a new physio-therapist (yes, *another*) shortly after. It was then followed by twelve sessions, once a week, of hospital gym, in which I was able to start working hard at getting my strength and mobility back. I had been told it might take a year to feel normal again, and one thing that my surgery recovery had taught me so far was to take one day at a time. In other words, not to rush. Not to worry about my rate of improvement. Just focus on today and do what today needs. I did just that for twelve weeks. The physiotherapist seemed quite amazed at my progress, having often dealt with older people recovering from hip replacements. Just the fact that within three weeks I was able to sit down on the floor meant that I had a far greater scope of stretches and exercises available to me to heal and strengthen.

Now, these days, I am on my own – in regard to the operation, that is; I will still see my rheumatologist. I do not need to see the surgeon for review for another ten years.

People ask me, "Are you all better now?" It's a difficult question, because I want to say yes, but the answer is still technically no. Yes, my hip is better, even if there will always be limitations. But no, my ankylosing spondylitis is not better. It cannot be cured by the doctors. So my hope is not in them. My hope is in my great physician, Jesus, who knows what's going on inside my body more clearly than any scan or test could show. He knows my journey in more detail than my words could hope to explain. He has been my hope, my joy and my strength throughout this whole journey.

I used to think that hope was a bit of a weak notion; some kind of wishful thinking that things could go the way I wanted them to, based on my own self-seeking desire. That is the world's idea of hope, but that is not what hope is. Hope in God is a sure thing. It is based on his unfailing truth and love. God is love, and he cannot be anything but what he is. Hoping in God doesn't mean that everything goes my way and nothing can touch me. The Bible actually promises we will have trouble in life. Even Jesus, who understood hope in God, experienced suffering in every way. So, what can we hope for? When we put our hope in Jesus, he says we are adopted into the family of God – God being the picture of a perfect father. A good dad does not bubble-wrap their kids and keep them from making decisions; a good dad allows freedom but gives wisdom and provision where it is needed. When a child has their dad there, they know they are safe. Dad sees the big picture and makes good plans that the child does not need to worry about figuring out, because Dad already knows what is best. My hope in God is when I say, "Dad, your plans are always better than mine, and if you can make the universe out of the power of your words, then you can make something incredible out of the nothings in my life." That kind of hope far outweighs, "I hope I get to have a decent holiday this year."

> *May the God of hope fill you with all joy and peace in believing, so that by the power of the Holy Spirit you may abound in hope.*
>
> *Romans 15:13*

During the weeks at the gym, my rheumatologist requested that I would have a blood test, which in the end confirmed that I can reduce my medication injections to once every three weeks, rather than every two weeks. That was great news, as it showed that all was continuing to work well and effectively in my body. It also means that I can travel for longer in the future, as I am less restricted by the amount of medication that I have available.

The last six years have been a journey of many highs and lows. I am probably physically in the best position that I have been over that time. Yes, I am no longer supposed to get back into the habit of running or do high-impact activities. My neck still clicks, cracks and only turns half the distance that it should. But I am close to pain-free and, as I mentioned previously, I know that there is a bright season ahead of me with new possibilities and adventures.

I am continuing to work freelance, but time will tell how long that remains viable. I am blessed to do a job where that has been an option for me, as for many people it is not.

I feel that this writing is perhaps the first chapter of my story. I know that it's not over yet. If you are battling a chronic condition, then the same goes for you. Your story is not over yet. What I mean to say is, there are good things ahead of you. The person you once were is not lost. You are still you. The hopes and dreams that were once in your heart are still there deep down for a reason.

Recently, our church had a few weeks focused on prayer. We had an evening when we were all praying loudly and intently, so much so that for a few moments it was at the top of our voices. I started coughing, as always seems to happen if I shout at the top of my lungs. My throat literally cannot take it. It gets irritated and causes me to cough. I used to get frustrated that I couldn't shout if I ever wanted to and prayed that I would be able to. This time I thought again, "I want to shout! I need my battle cry!" and I suddenly felt the reply in my heart, "But I made you to dance." I instantly felt OK with that. More than OK, I was relieved. We aren't created to look alike or be the same. We are created as a unique expression, with gifts and desires. I went home and danced in my living room. It felt as though it was what I was made to do. I was reminded that not so long ago I had thought that I might never do it. But here I was... dancing again. And there are other things I will do again. I will travel for more than just a few weeks. I will climb mountains. I will speak what's on my heart.

Afterword

What dreams are in your heart that have been pushed aside by the circumstances of life?

Where do you find your hope and what determines it?

There is hope for you. There is purpose. There is more. You may not have a chronic illness, or had any similar experience, but you've had your own journey to walk and battles to fight. I pray that in reading this, you will come to know joy in the highs and lows of your life. A joy that gives you strength. A joy that gives you peace.

An unjustified joy.

What Shall I Read Next?

God of Miracles
Sue Collins
ISBN 978-1-911086-88-8

Sue is an ordinary Christian mother who finds herself passing through the dark and devastating storms of baby bereavement twice in a single year. Through the events that follow and her encounters with the God of miracles, she eventually reaches a place of acceptance and discovers true peace, hope and finally joy. Sue's story will bring hope and encouragement to others affected by the loss of a baby or raising a child with special needs.

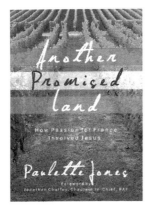

Another Promised Land
Paulette Jones
ISBN 978-1-910197-12-7

"Like many families, we very much looked forward to our holidays and the precious time to step off of the treadmill and relax together. Both our children were particularly enjoying languages at school so we decided help their studies and renew our love of France…"
Thus begins a voyage of discovery into French culture, customs and cuisine – and a deep sense of belonging. But when a mystery sickness takes hold of Paulette's life, her dreams and hopes are gradually stripped away. Eventually she finds herself alone in a small hamlet, unable to work, suffering intense pain and with many difficult questions. Filled with humorous anecdotes and sharp insights about life in France, Paulette's testimony demonstrates how God can restore our lives – not only for our good but for the blessing of the many people we encounter along the way.

Available from all good bookshops and from the publisher:
www.onwardsandupwards.org